D1373245

Roads to Reasoning

Developing Thinking Skills Through Problem Solving

Stephen Krulik and
Jesse A. Rudnick

Wright Group
McGraw-Hill

Acknowledgments

Project Editors
Mary Euretig, Darlene York

Writers
Stephen Krulik, Jesse A. Rudnick

Design Director
Karen Stack

Cover Design and Illustration
Aki Nurosi

Design
Gerta Sorensen

Illustration
Susan Aiello Studio

Composition
Graphic Advantage, Ltd.

© 2001 by Wright Group/McGraw-Hill
Two Prudential Plaza
Chicago, IL 60601

ISBN 0-7622-1351-5
Customer Service 800-624-0822
www.creativepublications.com

1 2 3 4 5 6 7 8 VHG 06 05 04 03 02 01

Contents

Introduction

Rationale

MOST MATHEMATICS EDUCATORS AGREE that the development of reasoning power is a primary objective of elementary mathematics. In fact, problem solving, which is the basis for developing reasoning power, has been at the forefront of the mathematics curriculum for many years. The National Council of Teachers of Mathematics' *Principles and Standards,* released in 2000, continues to emphasize both of these areas. Within the thinking and reasoning domain, the area that requires the greatest attention is the development of higher order thinking skills, specifically critical and creative thinking.

Critical thinking is the ability to analyze a situation and draw appropriate and correct conclusions from the given data. It includes determining inconsistent data, missing data, and extraneous information.

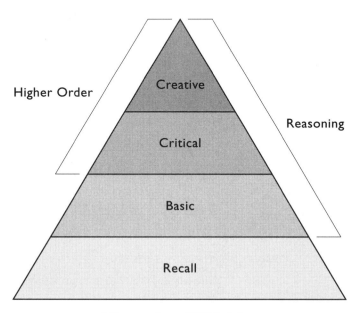

Hierarchy of Thinking

© Creative Publications 0-7622-1351-5

Creative thinking is the ability to originate a solution to a problem situation. In addition, it is the ability to generate, synthesize, and apply original ideas to produce a complex product.

Reasoning is the ultimate goal of the books in this series. Problem solving is the road that will lead to an increased ability to reason. The problems in this book are vehicles that carry the students along the road, and the teacher is the driver who guides the students.

Most mathematics textbook series include some degree of problem solving. This series provides additional practice using a variety of approaches that will further develop reasoning power. As students experience a variety of strategies for solving problems, they will become more flexible in their thinking and reasoning.

There is a strong connection between the problems in this series and the language arts—reading, writing, listening, and speaking. Careful reading of a word problem is often as important as mathematical skills for successfully solving the problem. It is critical that students

1) read the problem carefully,

2) find out what they are being asked to do,

3) solve the problem, and

4) determine whether or not the answer makes sense.

What's in This Book?

This book contains six sections, each of which focuses on a specific aspect of the problem-solving process and is designed to strengthen a particular reasoning skill.

Section 1: What Number Makes Sense?

This section contains problems and solutions from which numerical data has been removed. Students choose from a list of numbers to fill in the blanks so that the problems and solutions make sense.

Section 2: What's Wrong?

In this section students are given problems with solutions that contain errors in reasoning. The students identify the errors in reasoning and find the correct solutions to the problems.

Section 3: What Would You Do?

This section features open-ended problem situations. In each case, students solve the problem based upon their experiences, knowledge of the situation, and individual preference, and then support their solutions.

Section 4: What Questions Can You Answer?

This section contains mathematical settings with numerical data. Students generate a list of questions that can be answered based on the data and then answer at least one of their questions.

Section 5: What's Missing?

Each problem in this section is missing data required to solve the problem. Students identify what is missing, supply appropriate data, and then solve the problem.

© Creative Publications 0-7622-1351-5

Section 6: What's the Question if You Know the Answer?

This section contains problem situations that include data, but no questions. Students are given several possible answers for which they must supply appropriate questions.

How to Use This Book

Each section begins with a teaching lesson that walks students through a problem similar to the rest of the problems in the section. Suggested questions are provided. Responses generated in discussion during the teaching lesson allow students an opportunity to share their thinking and listen to the thinking of their peers. These discussions help students clarify their understanding of the process for solving the problems in the section.

The teaching lessons are designed to guide students as they are learning procedures. Depending on the needs of your students, you may also want to consider using other problems in a section for whole-group lessons. A great deal of interesting dialogue and thoughtful questioning can occur during these whole-class lessons.

The problems in this book can be used in a variety of ways.

Class Opener or Warm Up
Present the problem as an opening exercise to involve students in a discussion that can carry over into the day's lesson.

Class Closer
If there are a few minutes left at the end of a class period, introduce a problem in class and assign it as a homework or a family activity. Have students discuss the work at the beginning of the next day.

Small-Group or Partners Activity

After you have introduced a section with the teaching lesson, most students will be able to solve the remaining problems with a partner or in a small group. Working in this way, students can share their thinking with their peers and get important feedback.

Individual Activity

After students have participated in the teaching lesson and worked with a partner or small group, many will be ready to solve additional problems individually. The ability to work these problems independently may vary from student to student.

Assessment

Suggested answers to problems in this book can be found at the end of each section. However, you might prefer using a rubric to evaluate students' reasoning. You might even decide to check one section, or certain problems within a section, using the answer key and to assess other sections or problems within a section using a rubric.

A rubric is helpful in assessing a student's mathematical proficiency in relationship to specific criteria. A rubric can also help to more reliably assess complex student work. It can be used to evaluate various dimensions of mathematical activity such as problem solving, communication, use of mathematical language, reasoning, and number sense.

 © Creative Publications 0-7622-1351-5

The following general 3-point rubric can be used with any problem in any section of this book. If you prefer, feel free to develop your own rubric to provide for a more specific assessment. When using a rubric, it is recommended that you discuss the criteria with your students ahead of time. Doing so will help students to understand what a complete response should include and will encourage them to take time to reflect on their answers.

3	The student accomplishes the purpose of the question or task. Understanding of the mathematics in the task is demonstrated and the student is able to communicate his reasoning.
2	The student partially accomplishes the purpose of the question or task. Understanding of the mathematics may not be complete OR the student may not be able to communicate his reasoning adequately.
1	The student is not able to accomplish the purpose of the question or task. Understanding of the mathematics is fragmented and the communication is vague or incomplete.

Section 1 **What Number Makes Sense?**

In this section, students are presented with problem situations from which numerical data is missing. A set of numbers is provided and students determine where to place each number so the situation makes sense.

It is suggested that the teaching problem that follows be used as a whole-class activity.

The procedures outlined in the teaching problem will help students understand how to

a) carefully read the numerical situation,

b) decide which numbers to place in each blank,

c) determine whether the numbers they chose make sense.

The group interaction that occurs during the lesson will provide an opportunity for students to explain their thinking.

Consider having students work the first few problems that follow the teaching problem either with a partner or in a small group. After they have had a chance to become comfortable working with this type of problem, students can complete the remaining problems independently.

As they work through the exercises here, students practice computation and increase their repertoire of problem-solving skills. Reasoning skills are improved by being exposed to a variety of ways to solve a problem. Be sure to engage students in a class discussion after each problem has been completed so they can hear ways of solving problems that differ from their own.

Mathematical Skills
....

Teaching Problem
Addition, Subtraction

Problem 1
Fractions, Computation

Problem 2
Multiplication, Subtraction, Division

Problem 3
Time, Computation

Problem 4
Money, Division

Problem 5
Addition, Subtraction

Problem 6
Money, Subtraction, Addition

Problem 7
Geometry, Money

Problem 8
Number Sense, Multiplication, Division

Problem 9
Addition, Subtraction, Multiplication

Problem 10
Division, Multiplication

Jumbo Jet

Teaching Goal

After participating in this lesson, students will be able to solve the problem by identifying and accurately placing the missing information. Students will also be able to explain their reasoning and defend their answer.

Problem

On a jumbo jet, there were _____ seats, of which _____ were occupied. There were also _____ flight attendants and a crew of _____ members in the cockpit. Altogether, there were _____ people on board the aircraft.

7   15   308   330   340

Teaching Plan

1. Present the problem to the students.

2. Have students read the problem individually or read it together as a class.

3. Ask students to think about the problem. Ask what they need to do to solve the problem.

4. Ask students what information is given in the problem that helps them solve it. For example, does the term "altogether" provide any clues?

5. Have the students put the numbers in the blanks where they think they best fit.

6. Have students read the problem again to see if their answers make sense.

7. Lead a whole-group discussion. Consider using the following questions as part of the discussion:

How many seats would there be on the plane? 340

What would the total number of passengers on board the jumbo jet be? 308

Would it be possible in this problem for the number of passengers to be 340 and the number of seats to be 330? Why or why not? No. There cannot be more passengers than there are seats.

Could the total number of people on board the aircraft be 330? Yes, because when you add the passengers, flight attendants and crew you get a total of 330.

How many of the seats would be filled with passengers? 308

How many flight attendants would there be? 15

How many crewmembers might there be in the cockpit? 7

Would it be likely for the number of crewmembers in the cockpit to be 15 and the number of flight attendants to be 7? No. There are usually fewer people in the cockpit than in the cabin because the cockpit is such a small area.

Explain how you know you have the numbers in the correct blanks.

What strategy did you use?

Do you think your strategy will work for other problems of this kind?

. . . .

This think and check problem-solving process, along with class discussion allows students to use, extend, and communicate their reasoning and logic skills.

Problem 1 **The Taxi Trip**

A taxi charges _____ for the first

$\frac{1}{5}$ mile and _____ for each additional

$\frac{1}{5}$ mile. Ed paid _____ for his trip.

He traveled _____ miles in the taxi.

| $0.70 $1.15 $7.45   2 |

1. First, read the problem.

2. Look at the numbers in the box.

3. Put the numbers in the blanks where you think they fit best.

4. Read the problem again. Do the numbers make sense?

5. Explain how you know you have the numbers in the correct blanks.

_____

_____

_____

_____

_____

_____

© Wright Group/McGraw-Hill 0-7622-1351-5

Problem 2 **Picnic Beverages**

Dunbar Middle School ordered _____ bottles

of fruit juice from the local grocery store for its annual

picnic. The grocer ordered _____ cases of fruit

juice from the distributor. Each case contained

_____ bottles. The grocer had _____ bottles

of fruit juice left after the delivery to the school.

| 10 | 12 | 30 | 350 |

1. First, read the problem.

2. Look at the numbers in the box.

3. Put the numbers in the blanks where you think they fit best.

4. Read the problem again. Do the numbers make sense?

5. Explain how you know you have the numbers in the correct blanks.

_____

_____

_____

_____

Name
....

Problem 3 **Jan's School Schedule**

Jan attends Washington Middle School.

Her school day begins at _____ a.m.

The first period is a _____ minute

homeroom followed by _____ class

periods of _____ minutes each. She

also has a _____ minute lunch break.

Her school day ends at _____ p.m.

| 7 | 20 | 30 | 50 | 3:10 | 8:30 |

1. First, read the problem.

2. Look at the numbers in the box.

3. Put the numbers in the blanks where you think they fit best.

4. Read the problem again. Do the numbers make sense?

5. Explain how you know you have the numbers in the correct blanks.

_____

_____

_____

_____

© Wright Group/McGraw-Hill 0-7622-1351-5

Name
....

Problem 4 **The Little League Raffle**

Ralph's little league team sold _____ raffle

tickets for _____ each. The grand prize was

_____ , and it was shared equally by _____

people. When the money was divided, each

person received _____ .

5	$50.00	$1.00	$250.00	500

1. First, read the problem.

2. Look at the numbers in the box.

3. Put the numbers in the blanks where you think they fit best.

4. Read the problem again. Do the numbers make sense?

5. Explain how you know you have the numbers in the correct blanks.

_____

_____

_____

_____

Name
....

Problem 5 **Movie Attendance**

A new science fiction movie opened on Tuesday.

On opening night, only _____ people attended.

On Wednesday _____ more people came to

the movie than had come on Tuesday. On Thursday

attendance was down again when only _____

people came to see the movie. The total attendance

for the three days was _____.

47	**80**	**61**	**249**

1. First, read the problem.

2. Look at the numbers in the box.

3. Put the numbers in the blanks where you think they fit best.

4. Read the problem again. Do the numbers make sense?

5. Explain how you know you have the numbers in the correct blanks.

_____

_____

_____

_____

Problem 6 **The Baseball Game**

Michael went to a baseball game on
June _____. He took _____ dollars
with him. He spent _____ dollars for
a hot dog and a soda. He also bought a
T-shirt for _____ dollars. When Michael
got home, he had _____ dollars left.

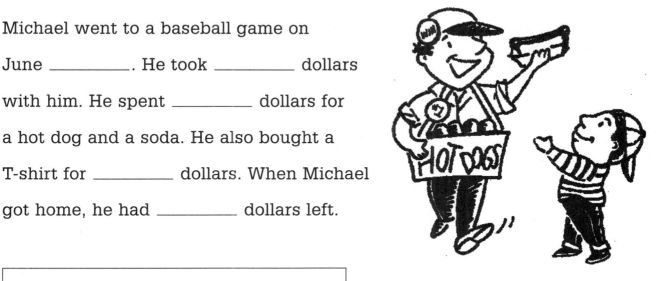

| 5 | 11 | 15 | 29 | 31 |

1. First, read the problem.

2. Look at the numbers in the box.

3. Put the numbers in the blanks where you think they fit best.

4. Read the problem again. Do the numbers make sense?

5. Explain how you know you have the numbers in the correct blanks.

_____

_____

_____

_____

Name
....

Problem 7 **The Cost of Corkboard**

The perimeter of a rectangular piece of corkboard

is _____ inches. Its length is _____ inches,

and its width is _____ inches. If corkboard

costs _____ per square foot, the cost of this

piece would be _____ .

12	24	72	$4.25	$8.50

1. First, read the problem.

2. Look at the numbers in the box.

3. Put the numbers in the blanks where you think they fit best.

4. Read the problem again. Do the numbers make sense?

5. Explain how you know you have the numbers in the correct blanks.

_____

_____

_____

_____

Name
....

Problem 8 **Breakfast for Champions**

The chef for the Olympic Village is in charge of

preparing breakfast for approximately _____

athletes who eat breakfast every morning.

Breakfast is usually served from _____ :00 a.m.

until _____ :00 a.m. each day. The chef

and his crew of _____ use approximately

_____ dozen eggs each morning.

| 6 | 9 | 17 | 90 | 500 |

1. First, read the problem.

2. Look at the numbers in the box.

3. Put the numbers in the blanks where you think they fit best.

4. Read the problem again. Do the numbers make sense?

5. Explain how you know you have the numbers in the correct blanks.

_____

_____

_____

_____

Name

....

Problem 9 **Temperature Changes**

At the base of the mountain, the temperature was

_____ degrees. As Justin climbed the mountain,

it became _____ degrees cooler every _____

feet. After climbing _____ feet, it was a cool

_____ degrees.

| 6 62 92 100 500 |

1. First, read the problem.

2. Look at the numbers in the box.

3. Put the numbers in the blanks where you think they fit best.

4. Read the problem again. Do the numbers make sense?

5. Explain how you know you have the numbers in the correct blanks.

_____

_____

_____

_____

© Wright Group/McGraw-Hill 0-7622-1351-5

Name
....

Problem 10 **Price Points**

The local card store sells birthday party invitations

for _____ each, and a box of _____ sells

for _____. A box of _____ ball point pens

sells for _____, or _____ for each pen.

| $0.40 | $0.50 | $2.40 | $3.50 | 6 | 7 |

---

1. First, read the problem.

2. Look at the numbers in the box.

3. Put the numbers in the blanks where you think they fit best.

4. Read the problem again. Do the numbers make sense?

5. Explain how you know you have the numbers in the correct blanks.

_____

_____

_____

_____

_____

Answer Key

Problem 1: The Taxi Trip
$1.15, $0.70, $7.45, 2

Problem 2: Picnic Beverages
350 bottles, 30 cases, 12 bottles,
10 left
or 350 bottles, 12 cases, 30 bottles,
10 left

Problem 3: Jan's School Schedule
8:30 a.m., 20 minute, 7 class
periods, 50 minutes, 30 minute,
3:10 p.m.

**Problem 4: The Little League
Raffle**
500 tickets, $1.00 each, $250.00,
5 people, $50.00

Problem 5: Movie Attendance
61, 47, 80, 249

Problem 6: The Baseball Game
29, 31, 5, 15, 11,
or 29, 31, 5, 11, 15

**Problem 7: The Cost
of Corkboard**
72 inches, 24 inches, 12 inches,
$4.25, $8.50
or 72 inches, 12 inches, 24 inches,
$4.25, $8.50

**Problem 8: Breakfast
for Champions**
500 athletes, 6 a.m., 9 a.m.,
17 crew members, 90 dozen

**Problem 9: Temperature
Changes**
92 degrees, 6 degrees, 100 feet,
500 feet, 62 degrees

Problem 10: Price Points
$0.50, 7, $3.50, 6, $2.40, $0.40
or $0.40, 6, $2.40, 7, $3.50, $0.50

Assessment Note
Student work on any of the
problems in this section can be
assessed using the 3-step rubric
on page viii.

Section 2 What's Wrong?

EACH PROBLEM THAT IS PRESENTED in this section has been solved, but the solution is incorrect. An error has been made either in concept, interpretation, or computation. Students must identify the error that was made and find the correct solution to the problem.

It is recommended that the teaching problem that follows be used as a whole-class activity.

The procedures outlined in the teaching problem will take students through the process of

a) finding the correct solution to the problem,

b) identifying the error that was made.

Consider having students work the first few problems that follow the teaching problem either with a partner or in a small group. This will provide an opportunity for them to become comfortable working with this type of problem. The remaining pages might then be assigned for students to complete independently.

This section deals with error analysis. Each exercise offers an effective means for students to practice computation skills within a problem-solving context. Different strategies such as drawing diagrams or pictures, writing an equation, or creating a table or graph may be used to solve problems. By engaging in class discussion after a problem has been completed, students will be able to hear ways of solving problems that differ from their own. The group interaction that occurs during these discussions often leads to deeper mathematical understanding.

Section 2

Ball Park Prizes

Teaching Goal

After participating in this lesson, students will be able to identify a reasoning error presented in the problem. Students will also choose a representation, either visual or numerical, and use it to solve the problem.

Problem

> When Tomas attended the game at the new stadium, he was one of 16,000 people in the crowd. The first 2,000 people received gifts. Half of the people received caps, half of the remaining people received bats, and the rest received T-shirts. Tomas figured he would receive a gift.
>
> Tomas's thinking ▶
>
> $\frac{1}{2} \times 2,000 = 1,000$ 1,000 people received caps
> $\frac{1}{2} \times 1,000 = 500$ +   500 people received bats
>   1,500 people received caps or bats
>
> $16,000 - 1,500 = 14,500$
> 14,500 people received T-shirts

Teaching Plan

1. Present the problem to the students.

2. Have students read the problem.

3. Lead a whole-group discussion. Consider using the following questions as part of the discussion. (A table might be a convenient way to display the data).

What information given in the problem is helpful for solving it? The number of people who received gifts, and how the gifts to be received were determined

What information given in the problem is unnecessary for solving it? The entire attendance of 16,000 people

How many people received gifts? 2,000 people

Of the 2,000 people, how many received caps? 1,000 people

Of the 2,000, how many received bats? 500 people

How many people have now received a gift? 1,500

How many of the 2,000 will get a T-shirt? 500 people

What is the mistake in Tomas's thinking? Tomas used the total attendance to determine how many people would receive T-shirts, but only the first 2,000 people received a gift.

How could you correct Tomas's error? Subtract 1,500 from 2,000

Does anyone have a different strategy?

. . . .

You may wish to encourage students to use a specific representation to solve the different problems in this section. You may also have them try using multiple representations, for example, making a drawing and writing an equation to solve one or more of the problems.

Problem 1 **Climbing Lizard**

A lizard was attempting to climb a slippery three-foot tree. He started on the ground and at first climbed to 12 inches from the top of the tree. He slipped back 6 inches. He then climbed back up 9 inches and slipped back 2 inches. Not a lizard to give up easily, he then climbed up 3 inches and slipped back 5 inches. Jamila figures that the lizard is 11 inches from the ground.

Jamila's thinking ▶ $12 + 9 + 3 = 24$
$6 + 2 + 5 = 13$ and
$24 - 13 = 11$

There is something wrong with Jamila's thinking.

1. Show how to get the correct solution.

2. Explain the error in Jamila's thinking.

_____

_____

Name
....

Problem 2 **Supermarket Shopping**

Georgia went to the supermarket.
She bought two boxes of cereal for $3.20
each, one container of milk for $2.10,
one box of laundry detergent for $4.50,
and a tube of toothpaste for $2.35.
She had a cereal coupon for $0.50, a
soap coupon for $0.40, and a toothpaste
coupon for $0.25. The store doubles
each coupon. Here is her receipt.

There is something wrong with the
receipt.

Cereal	$ 3.20
Cereal	$ 3.20
Milk	$ 2.10
Laundry detergent	$ 4.50
Toothpaste	$ 2.35
Subtotal	$15.35
Coupon $0.50	
$\times$ 2	− $ 1.00
Coupon $0.40	
$\times$ 2	− $ 0.80
Total	$13.55

1. Give the correct total and show how you would find it.

```



```

2. Explain the error made in the receipt.

_____

_____

_____

Name
....

Problem 3 **Pizza Dinner**

The Sorensen family ordered a large pizza for dinner. The pizza was cut into eight equal slices. Andrew ate three slices of the pizza, and his sister, Suzanne, ate two slices. Mr. Sorensen asked Andrew if he knew what fraction of the pizza he and his sister had eaten.

Andrew's thinking ▶ I ate 3 of the 8 pieces. That's $\frac{3}{8}$.
Suzanne ate 2 of the 8 pieces. That's $\frac{2}{8}$.
$\frac{3}{8} + \frac{2}{8} = \frac{5}{16}$.
Together, we ate $\frac{5}{16}$ of the pizza.

There is something wrong with Andrew's thinking.

1. Show how you would solve the problem.

2. Explain the error made in Andrew's thinking.

_____

_____

_____

© Wright Group/McGraw-Hill 0-7622-1351-5

Permission is given by the publisher to reproduce this page for classroom or home use only.

Name
....

Problem 4 **Football-Kicking Contest**

In a football-kicking contest, Alice kicked the football 60 feet. Hannah kicked the football 12 feet farther than Alice did. Maya kicked the ball halfway between the spots where the other two balls had landed. Maya figured she kicked the ball 24 feet.

Maya's thinking ▶ $60 - 12 = 48$
$\frac{1}{2}$ of $48 = 24$

There is something wrong with Maya's thinking.

1. Show how you would solve the problem.

2. Explain the error in Maya's thinking.

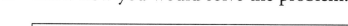

Name
....

Problem 5 **Cutting Time**

Jerry is a carpenter. He can cut a plank into six pieces in
ten minutes. Jerry figures that working at the same rate,
it would take him 20 minutes to cut the plank into 12 pieces.

Jerry's thinking ▶
**6 cuts take 10 minutes.
There are twice as many pieces,
so it will take twice as long to cut them.
12 cuts will take 20 minutes.**

There is something wrong with Jerry's thinking.

1. Show how you would solve the problem.

2. Explain the error in Jerry's thinking.

_____

_____

_____

   © Wright Group/McGraw-Hill 0-7622-1351-5

Name
....

Problem 6 **Money Owed**

Taylor already owed Katherine $2.20 when the two girls agreed to buy a $10.00 CD and split the cost equally. Katherine paid for the CD. Taylor figures she now owes Katherine $6.10.

Taylor's thinking ▶

$$\$10.00 + \$2.20 = \$12.20$$
$$\$12.20 \div 2 = \$6.10$$

There is something wrong with Taylor's thinking.

1. Show how you would solve the problem.

```


```

2. Explain the error in Taylor's thinking.

_____

_____

_____

Name
....

Problem 7 **Museum Trip**

Two classes from Lincoln Middle School went on a trip to the museum. Altogether, thirty-five people went on the trip. Two adults and five students were assigned to ride in each van. The coordinator of the trip figured there would be fourteen adults.

Coordinator's thinking ▶

> Let x equal the number of adults for each bus.
> $$\frac{2}{5} \diagup\!\!\!\!\!\diagdown \frac{x}{35}$$
> $$5x = 70$$
> $$5x \div 5 = 70 \div 5$$
> $$x = 14$$
> There are 14 adults.

There is something wrong with the picnic coordinator's thinking.

1. Show how you would solve the problem.

[   ]

2. Explain the error in the coordinator's thinking.

_____

_____

Name

....

Problem 8 **Making Outfits**

Louis has three different shirts and four different pairs
of pants. He can wear any shirt with any pair of pants.
He figures he can create seven different outfits.

Louis's thinking ▶

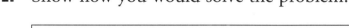

3 shirts + 4 pants = 7 outfits

There is something wrong with Louis's thinking.

1. Show how you would solve the problem.

2. Explain the error in Louis's thinking.

_____

_____

_____

Problem 9 **Consecutively Numbered Cube**

Mrs. Gallo assigned this homework problem to her math class:

> I have a cube whose faces are marked with consecutive numbers. Three of the faces are numbered 28, 30, and 32. What is the sum of the six numbers on the cube?

Devonne solved the problem and came up with an answer of 183. When Devonne gave the same problem to his father to solve, his father came up with an answer of 177.

There is something wrong with the homework problem.

1. Show how you would solve the problem.

2. Explain what's wrong with the homework problem.

_____

_____

_____

Name
....

Problem 10 **Printing Costs**

Mr. Olsen needed 3,800 brochures printed for his new business. The clerk at the print shop asked Mr. Olsen if he would like to order 4,000 brochures in order to take advantage of the price break. Mr. Olsen decided not to change his order because he thought getting so many extra brochures would wind up costing him more money.

There is something wrong with Mr. Olsen's thinking.

1. Show how you would solve the problem.

2. Explain the error in Mr. Olsen's thinking.

_____

_____

_____

_____

Answer Key

Problem 1: Climbing Lizard
If he climbed 12 inches from the top of a 36 inch post, he would be at 24 inches. So he went up $24 + 9 + 3 = 36$ and slid down a total of $6 + 2 + 5 = 13$ inches. Therefore, he would be at $36 - 13$ or 23 inches from the ground.

Problem 2: Supermarket Shopping
The clerk neglected to give Georgia credit for the toothpaste coupon. The total should have been $0.50 less, or $13.05.

Problem 3: Pizza Dinner
Andrew added the denominators. The denominators tell what size the fractions are. Both fractions were eighths, so the denominator should have been eighths. He should have just added the numerators. The correct solution is $\frac{3}{8} + \frac{2}{8} = \frac{5}{8}$.

Problem 4: Football-Kicking Contest
Hannah kicked the ball 72 feet, 12 feet farther than Alice. Halfway between 60 and 72 feet would be 66 feet. A drawing would help in solving this problem:

$$\begin{array}{c} \vdash\!\!-\!\!-\!\!-\!\!-\!\!-\!\!-\!\!-\!\!-\!\!|\!\!-\!\!-\!|\!\!-\!\!| \\ 0 \qquad 60\text{ ft}\quad 66\text{ ft}\quad 72\text{ ft} \end{array}$$

Problem 5: Cutting Time
Cutting the board into six pieces only requires five cuts. Each cut took two minutes. Cutting the board into 12 pieces will require 11 cuts, or 22 minutes.

Problem 6: Money Owed
Taylor owes Katherine $5.00 for her share of the CD, plus the $2.20 she previously owed her. She should give Katherine $7.20.

Problem 7: Museum Trip
The coordinator compared the number of adults to the number of students. The comparison should have been the number of adults to the total population on each bus. The correct number was 10 adults.

Problem 8: Making Outfits
There are 12 possible outfits or combinations. Students could multiply $3 \times 4 = 12$, or they could make a tree diagram or list.

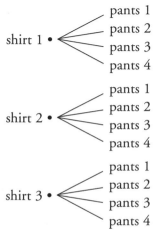

Problem 9: Consecutively Numbered Cube
The question does not tell which number on the cube is the largest or the smallest, so more than one answer is possible. Both answers are correct. Devonne's father assumed that 32 was the largest number on the cube, and he added the sequence
$27 + 28 + 29 + 30 + 31 + 32$
to get 177.
Devonne used the sequence
$28 + 29 + 30 + 31 + 32 + 33$
to get 183.

Problem 10: Printing Costs
Mr. Olsen did not realize that it would be cheaper to order 4,000 brochures.
$3,800 \times \$0.14 = \$532.00$, and $4,000 \times \$0.104 = \$416.00$. He may not have renamed 10.4¢ to a decimal properly, or he may have made a miscalculation when multiplying.

Assessment Note
Student work on any of the problems in this section can be assessed using the 3-step rubric on page viii.

Section 3 What Would You Do?

OPEN-ENDED PROBLEMS ARE PRESENTED in this section. In each case, after finding an answer, students are asked to support their solution.

These problems give students the opportunity to use their prior knowledge as a foundation on which to build and strengthen their skills. Both computation and problem-solving abilities are engaged.

Consider using the teaching problem format with the first few problems in the section. The next few might then be solved within small groups, and the remaining problems completed on an individual basis.

Group discussions about solutions provide an important forum for a valuable exchange of ideas. These discussions allow students to practice effective communication of their own mathematical thinking and to gain insights and understanding through listening to the solution strategies of others.

Equal Portions

Teaching Goal

After participating in this lesson, students will be able to use a number of tools such as their experiences, prior knowledge, and individual preferences to solve the problem. Students will also be able to support their answers using logic and reasoning.

Problem

Three friends were sharing a rectangular cake. They had already divided the cake into three equal portions as shown below, when another friend came along. They wanted to share the cake equally among all four friends.

Teaching Plan

1. Present the problem to the students.

2. Have the students read the problem.

3. Lead a whole-group discussion. Consider using the following questions as part of the discussion:

What would you do to the already cut cake so that all four friends could share it equally? There are many ways to resolve the situation. One method would involve making one additional cut to the cake. The cake has already been cut into thirds vertically. One horizontal cut across the cake, $\frac{1}{4}$ of the way down, would yield six pieces; the three smaller pieces would each equal $\frac{1}{12}$ of the cake, and the three larger pieces would each equal $\frac{3}{12}$ of the cake. There would be four portions, each equal to $\frac{3}{12}$, or $\frac{1}{4}$, of the cake.

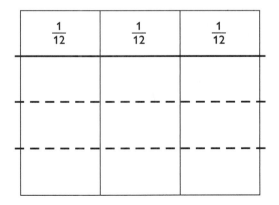

Explain your solution.

Is there another way to divide the cake equally? Explain.

Students may have different solutions, but they should be able to explain the choice they made.

· ·

Since the problems in this section are somewhat open-ended, there may be a variety of strategies and solutions. It is important to encourage students to choose a solution that they can defend.

Name
....

Problem 1 **Bridge Tolls**

To cross the local toll bridge, a
driver must pay a round-trip toll
of $2.00. However, a monthly
pass can be purchased for $30.00.

1. Which payment method would
you choose?

2. Explain the reasons for your choice.

_____

_____

_____

_____

_____

Name
....

Problem 2 **Advertising Fund**

You are in charge of the advertising budget for a sportswear company. You have a budget of $200,000 to spend each week on television advertising time. Advertising time is $5,000 per minute for prime time and $3,000 per minute for off time. Prime time is considered to be from 8:00 p.m. to 11:00 p.m. every day.

1. Make a schedule for your advertising budget for one week.

Include the days, times, and number of minutes each ad will run.

2. Explain how you made your choices.

_____

_____

_____

_____

Name
....

Problem 3 **Congratulations!**

You have just won $10,000 on the popular quiz show *Spend It or Lose It.* You must spend all of the money within 24 hours. Whatever you do not spend, you must give back.

1. What are some things you might buy? _____

_____

_____

_____

2. Estimate the cost of each item and give the total.

_____

_____

_____

_____

_____

_____

_____

_____

© Wright Group/McGraw-Hill 0-7622-1351-5

Problem 4 **Pet Care**

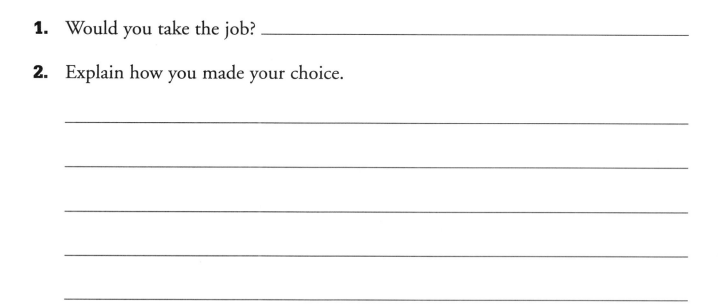

Your neighbor, Mrs. Jimenez, wants you to take care of her pets for 3 days. She will pay a total of $25.00. Mrs. Jimenez has two cats and one dog. There are a number of conditions.

a. The pets must be fed twice a day and given fresh water every day.

b. You must pay for the pet food yourself.

c. Each cat eats one small can of cat food each day.

d. The dog eats one large can of dog food each day.

e. A small can of cat food costs $0.89 and a large can of dog food costs $1.09.

1. Would you take the job? _____

2. Explain how you made your choice.

_____

_____

_____

_____

_____

Name

....

Problem 5 **Flight Choices**

Joseph was planning a trip from Chicago to Los Angeles.
He found the following flight information on the Internet:

a. Non-stop first class flight with lunch for $550.00

b. Coach flight with two stops that includes a 3-hour
    layover at each stop for $299.00

c. Coach flight with a plane change that includes
    a $2\frac{1}{2}$-hour layover and snack service for $475.00

1. Which flight would you choose? _____

2. Explain your choice.

_____

_____

_____

_____

_____

_____

_____

_____

© Wright Group/McGraw-Hill 0-7622-1351-5

Name

....

Problem 6 **Radio Hour**

You are the new disc jockey on the school radio station. You have a one-hour program every Saturday morning. During the hour, you must have eight commercials that last one-and-one-half minutes each. You can choose songs from the station's library containing twenty songs that last three minutes each, twenty songs that last three-and-one-half minutes each, and ten songs that last four minutes each.

1. Make a schedule for the hour including the placement of songs, commercials, and talk time.

2. Explain your choices.

_____

_____

_____

_____

Name
....

Problem 7 **Planting Plan**

On each side of the staircase at the entrance to your school, there is a rectangular plot that is eight feet long and three feet wide. The school wants flowers planted and you have been asked to plan the landscaping for each plot. All plants must have one foot of space between them. You have up to $125.00 to spend. The following plant types are available:

Plant Type	Color	Height	Cost
Calla Lily	Red	4 feet	$4.00 each
Pansies	Assorted	3 inches	$0.50 each
Ostrich Fern	Dark green	5 feet	$7.00 each
Azalea	Assorted	3 feet	$6.50 each
Lantana	Assorted	2 feet	$2.50 each
Tulips	Assorted	1 foot	$1.50 each
Daffodils	Yellow	$1\frac{1}{2}$ feet	$1.00 each

1. Draw a plan for the design of each rectangular area.

2. Figure the total cost for the plants you choose.

_____

_____

Name
....

Problem 8 **Similar Triangles**

You have a drawing of a triangle as shown.
You want to make a triangle that is exactly
the same shape, but with each side three
times the length of the original.

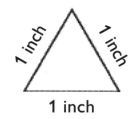

1 inch

1. Show how you would enlarge the triangle.

2. Explain the process you choose.

_____

_____

_____

Problem 9 **Vegetable Garden**

Your dad is helping you plant a vegetable
garden in your back yard. You want the
garden to be rectangular, and you have
80 feet of fence to enclose it. The choices
for the dimensions of the garden have been
narrowed to the following: 25 feet × 15 feet,
10 feet × 30 feet, or 20 feet × 20 feet.

1. Which dimensions would you choose? Explain your choice.

2. How many square feet of garden space would be created by each of the choices?

_____

_____

_____

_____

© Wright Group/McGraw-Hill 0-7622-1351-5

Problem 10 **Football Game**

You and two friends are planning to attend a local college football game. You will each need a ticket, and you would like to have some money left to buy snacks. Altogether, you have $50.00 to spend. The ticket and snack prices are listed.

Seating	
Box seats	$15.00
Lower reserved section	$12.00
Upper reserved section	$10.00
Bleacher seats	$ 7.50
Snacks	
Hot dog	$ 1.50
Soda	$ 1.00
Ice Cream	$ 1.25
Peanuts	$ 0.75

1. Which tickets would you buy?
Explain your choice.

_____

_____

_____

2. Show the total amount you would spend for tickets and food.
Also, include the amount of money you would have left.

_____

_____

_____

_____

Answer Key

Problems 1–10

Answers will vary. It is important that students have reasonable answers and explanations.

Problem 8: Similar Triangles

One strategy students might use would be to trace or draw the original figure on grid paper, then copy the figure onto grid paper with squares that have sides three times as long as the original. Another strategy would be to cut pieces of string three times the length of each side of the original triangle, then put the three longer pieces together to form the required triangle. Still another strategy would be to use a protractor to measure the angles at each end of the base. A triangle could be drawn with angles equal to those measurements, but with sides three times the length of the original. (In similar triangles, the corresponding angles are congruent.)

Assessment Note

Student work on any of the problems in this section can be assessed using the 3-step rubric on page viii.

Section 4 — What Questions Can You Answer?

IN THIS SECTION, STUDENTS ARE PRESENTED with situations that include numerical data and are asked to generate questions that can be answered from the data. There is a natural integration of language arts and mathematics as students analyze information, formulate and record their questions, and then find the answers to the questions they've created.

It is recommended that the teaching problem that follows be used as a whole-class activity.

The procedures outlined in the teaching problem will help students understand how to

a) identify the information that is given in the problem,

b) determine what kinds of questions can be constructed from the data,

c) find a solution to the questions posed.

Consider having students work the first few problems that follow the teaching problem with a partner or in small groups. This will allow them to brainstorm ideas to generate as many questions as possible. They can select their best questions to record on the student page and then work together to find the solutions. The remaining problems might then be assigned for students to work independently.

After students have completed working on a problem, be sure to discuss the questions generated as well as the answers. Such discussion can provide a valuable opportunity for students to hear the variety of questions posed.

Mathematical Skills

Teaching Problem
Data Analysis, Addition, Subtraction

Problem 1
Money, Addition, Subtraction, Multiplication

Problem 2
Addition, Subtraction

Problem 3
Money, Multiplication, Division, Subtraction

Problem 4
Fractions, Addition, Subtraction

Problem 5
Data Analysis, Addition, Subtraction

Problem 6
Money, Multiplication, Addition, Subtraction

Problem 7
Measurement, Fractions

Problem 8
Fractions, Division

Problem 9
Data Analysis, Addition, Subtraction, Averages

Problem 10
Probability

Accurate Survey Company

Teaching Goal

After participating in this lesson, students should be cognizant of the breadth and depth of questions that can be constructed with given data. They should also be able to find answers to questions they pose.

Problem

The Accurate Survey Company called 1,000 people on Monday night to find out what television program they were watching. The surveyors received the following responses.

Program	People Watching
Comedy Club	345
Football Game	193
Weeknight Movie	253
All others	170

Teaching Plan

1. Write the above information on the overhead projector, chalkboard, or white board.

2. Ask students to read the information.

3. Lead a whole-class discussion and include the following:

   What information are you given? The number of people who were watching each program on Monday night

When you see numbers and a problem like this, the teacher usually asks some questions about the numbers. Today you are going to get a chance to be the teacher and think of some questions that could be answered with the given information. Can you think of one?

One question that might be suggested is *How many people watched the Comedy Club on Monday night?* Record questions on the board. Encourage students to generate as many questions as possible.

4. Encourage students to create questions that will require mathematical calculations. For example:

How many more people watched the Comedy Club than the football game?

How many people watched the football game and the weeknight movie?

How many people are represented in the table?

How many people did not respond to the survey?

5. After students have generated an interesting variety of questions, invite them to find solutions.

How can you find out how many more people watched the Comedy Club than watched the football game?

How would you figure out how many people responded to the survey?

What strategy would you use to figure how many people did not respond to the survey?

....

Almost all students will be able to achieve some level of success with this lesson. The sophistication of questions posed depends on the developmental level of each student.

Name
....

Problem 1 **End-of-Year Party**

The food committee would like to serve tacos, juice, and frozen
yogurt bars for the end-of-year party. There are 27 students
in the class, and the budget for the party is $75.00. Tacos cost
$1.29 each. A quart of juice, which will supply four servings,
costs $2.09. Frozen yogurt bars are $0.69 each.

Write two questions you can answer about the cost of food for the party.

1. _____

_____

_____

2. _____

_____

_____

3. Find the answer to your first question. Show your work.

_____

_____

_____

_____

_____

Roads to Reasoning | Grade 5

....

Problem 2 **The Softball League**

Runs Scored in the Softball League

Game 1	Game 2	Game 3
Hurricanes ⊬⊬⊬⁻	Hurricanes ⊬⊬⊬⁻	Blizzards ⊬⊬⊬⁻
Blizzards ⊬⊬⊬⁻ ||	Tornadoes ||	Tornadoes 0

Write two questions you can answer about the points scored in the softball games.

1. _____

_____

_____

2. _____

_____

_____

3. Find the answer to your first question. Show your work.

_____

_____

_____

_____

Problem 3 **School Store**

Mr. Lopez wants to buy pencils to sell in the school store.
He can buy them for $0.15 each. He can also buy them in packages
of twenty for $2.50, or in boxes of one hundred for $10.00.

Write two questions you can answer about the pencils.

1. _____

_____

_____

2. _____

_____

_____

3. Find the answer to your first question. Show your work.

_____

_____

_____

_____

Name
. . . .

Problem 4 **Aquarium**

Alberto has 32 tropical fish in his
aquarium. Half of them are neon tetras,
one-fourth are mollies, one-eighth are
angelfish, and the rest are swordtails.

Write two questions you can answer
about the fish.

1. _____

_____

_____

2. _____

_____

_____

3. Find the answer to your first question. Show your work.

_____

_____

_____

_____

Problem 5 **Temperature Recordings**

The airport weather station records the outside temperature every hour. The table shows the daytime readings for one summer day.

Hour	7 am	8 am	9 am	10 am	11 am	12 pm	1 pm	2 pm	3 pm	4 pm	5 pm	6 pm
Temp	68°	70°	72°	76°	81°	85°	88°	90°	93°	93°	91°	89°

Write two questions you can answer about the weather.

1. _____

_____

_____

2. _____

_____

_____

3. Find the answer to your first question. Show your work.

_____

_____

_____

·····································

Problem 6 **The A.J. Appliance Store**

During August, the A.J. Appliance Store sold 25 air conditioners at an average price of $349.00. They sold 15 washing machines at an average price of $410.00 and 40 large screen television sets at an average price of $525.00. They also sold 80 CD players at an average price of $75.00.

Write two questions you can answer about the items that were sold.

1. _____

_____

_____

2. _____

_____

_____

3. Find the answer to your first question. Show your work.

_____

_____

_____

_____

Problem 7 **The Figure**

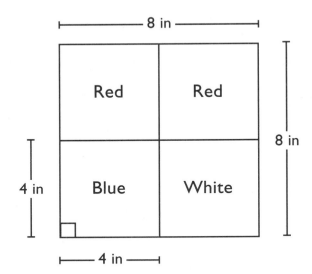

Write two questions you can answer about the figure.

1. _____

_____

_____

2. _____

_____

_____

3. Find the answer to your first question. Show your work.

_____

_____

_____

Problem 8 **Pizza for Three**

Three members of the gymnastics team shared a pizza after
the game. They bought a 14-inch pizza for $12.00. The pizza
was cut into eight equal slices. George ate four slices, Liz ate
three slices, and Maria only had one slice.

Write two questions you can answer about the pizza.

1. _____

_____

_____

2. _____

_____

_____

3. Find the answer to your first question. Show your work.

_____

_____

_____

_____

_____

Problem 9 **Test Scores**

	Test #1	Test #2	Test #3	Test #4	Test #5	Test #6
Sofia	85	78	72	91	85	88
Rachel	100	92	84	90	82	91

Write two questions you can answer about the girls' test scores.

1. _____

_____

_____

2. _____

_____

_____

3. Find the answer to your first question. Show your work.

_____

_____

_____

_____

_____

....

Problem 10 **Game Spinner**

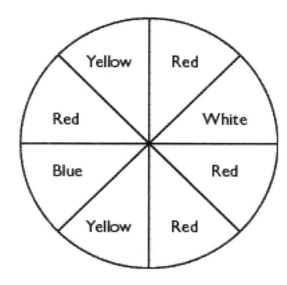

Write two probability questions you can answer about the spinner.

1. _____

_____

_____

2. _____

_____

_____

3. Find the answer to your first question. Show your work.

_____

_____

_____

Answer Key

In this section students write questions that can be answered with the information given. This answer key includes typical questions that might be written by students. Many other questions are possible.

Problem 1: End-of-Year Party
Possible questions
How much will it cost to buy a taco for each student in the class?

Will there be enough money to buy tacos, juice, and frozen yogurt bars for all the students?

How much will it cost to provide each student with a taco, frozen yogurt bar, and serving of juice?

Problem 2: The Softball League
Possible questions
How many points did the Hurricanes score in both of their games?

How many more total points did the Blizzards score than the Tornadoes?

Which team had the highest point total for the games played?

Problem 3: School Store
Possible questions
What is the cost of one pencil when buying a package of 20?

How much will Mr. Lopez save buying 60 pencils in packages rather than individually?

How much would it cost for Mr. Lopez to buy 15 pencils?

Problem 4: Aquarium
Possible questions
How many of each type of fish are in the aquarium?

How many more tetras are there than swordtails?

How many swordtails are in the aquarium?

Problem 5: Temperature Recordings
Possible questions
How much warmer was it at noon than it was at 8 a.m.?

Between which two hours was there the greatest rise in temperature?

What is the difference between the highest and the lowest temperatures?

Problem 6: The A.J. Appliance Store
Possible questions
What was the total amount on the sale of all air conditioners?

What was the total amount on the sales of all the CD players?

Did the store make more money in August selling air conditioners or washing machines?

Problem 7: The Figure
Possible questions
What fraction of the figure is blue?

What is the area of the figure?

What is the perimeter of each small square?

Problem 8: Pizza for Three
Possible questions
What fraction of the pizza did George eat?

What fraction of the pizza did Maria eat?

How could the gymnasts have divided the pizza equally?

Problem 9: Test Scores
Possible questions
Which girl had the higher overall score?

What is the difference between Sofia's highest and lowest test scores?

What is Rachel's average test score?

Problem 10: Game Spinner
Possible questions
What is the probability of landing on red?

What is the probability of landing on yellow?

What is the probability of landing on white?

Assessment Note
Students' work on any of the problems in this section can be assessed using the 3-step rubric on page viii.

Section 5 What's Missing?

IN THIS SECTION, STUDENTS ARE PRESENTED with problems that cannot be solved because an important piece of information has been omitted. Students must identify what is missing, supply appropriate data, and then solve the problem.

It is recommended that the teaching problem that follows be used as a whole-class activity.

The procedures outlined in the teaching problem will help students understand how to

a) identify the question that is asked,

b) determine the piece of information that is missing,

c) supply a number or other data that will enable them to solve the problem.

After the teaching problem, it is suggested that students work with a partner or in a small group, especially for the initial lessons. Once the majority of students are comfortable with the procedures, the remaining problems can be worked independently.

Group discussion of problems throughout this section is important, even after students are working independently. Because there is a wide range of data that students can supply to solve each problem, interesting discussions based on the specific data chosen are possible. Each different piece of missing information supplied by a student produces a different problem.

Mathematical Skills

....

Teaching Problem
Fractions, Computation

Problem 1
Multiplication, Addition

Problem 2
Addition with Decimals

Problem 3
Division, Subtraction

Problem 4
Measurement, Multiplication, Subtraction, Addition

Problem 5
Time, Computation

Problem 6
Division, Addition, Subtraction

Problem 7
Addition, Subtraction, Multiplication

Problem 8
Data Analysis, Multiplication, Addition

Problem 9
Multiplication, Addition, Subtraction

Problem 10
Division

Basketball Game

Teaching Goal

After participating in this lesson, students should be able to identify the missing piece of information that is preventing them from solving the problem. They should also be able to choose a number or other data that will enable them to solve the problem. They should understand that there is a range of possible numbers or data that could be used to solve the problem.

Problem

> In last night's basketball game, Josie was the leading scorer for the Falcons. She scored $\frac{1}{3}$ of the team's total score. Carla and Lucy each scored 9 points fewer than Josie. Three other team members scored the rest of the points. How many points were not scored by Josie, Carla, and Lucy?

Teaching Plan

1. Write the problem on the overhead projector, chalkboard, or whiteboard.

2. Have the students read the problem.

3. Lead a discussion with the whole class using the following questions as part of the discussion.

   What question is being asked? How many of the total points were not scored by Josie, Carla, and Lucy?

What information do you know from the problem? Josie scored $\frac{1}{3}$ of the team's total points. Carla and Lucy scored each scored nine points less than Josie.

Why can't you answer the question? The total number of points scored by the Falcons is not known.

If you know the number of points scored by the Falcons, could you answer the question? For example, if the Falcons scored 90 points, how many points did Josie score? 30: $\frac{1}{3}$ of 90 = 30.

How many points did Carla and Lucy score? 21: 30 − 9 = 21.

How many points did the three other team members score? 18: 90 − (30 + 21 + 21) = 18

Could you solve the problem if you knew how many points Josie scored? For example, if Josie scored 16 points, what is the total number of points the team scored? 48: 16 × 3 = 48

Now figure out the number of points Carla and Lucy scored.

7 each: 16 − 9 = 7.

How many points did the other three members score?

18: 48 − (16 + 7 + 7) = 18.

....

Repeat the above procedure using different numbers for the total number of points the team scored and for the number of points Josie scored. Students should see that they can solve the problem if they know either the total number of points the team scored OR the number of points Josie scored.

Problem 1 **Rolls of Film**

Anita used eight rolls of film to take pictures on a class
trip to Washington, D.C. Some of the rolls of film
contained 24 pictures and others contained 36 pictures.
How many pictures did she take on her trip?

1. What is the question? _____

_____

2. What information do you know from the problem? _____

_____

_____

3. What else do you need to know to solve the problem? _____

_____

_____

4. Pick numbers that will tell how many pictures were on each roll of film.

_____

5. Now find out how many pictures Anita took on her trip.

_____

_____

Name

....

Problem 2 **Rain Gauge**

Tao has a gauge to measure rainfall in
his back yard. He read the gauge before a
big storm. After one hour he noted that
0.65 inches of rain had fallen. During the
second hour another 0.45 inches had
fallen. At the end of the storm he noted
that an additional 0.7 inches had fallen.
What was the measure of the rain gauge
at the end of the storm?

1. What is the question? _____

_____

2. What information do you know from the problem? _____

_____

3. What else do you need to know to solve the problem? _____

_____

4. Pick a number that tells how much water was in the rain gauge at the

beginning of the storm. _____

5. Now what would the rain gauge measure at the end of the storm?

_____

Problem 3 **The County Fair**

Gloria and Alex went to the County Fair. Gloria bought
a book of 10 tickets for $8.50, and Alex bought a larger
economy book of tickets for $16.00. How much less
did each ticket in Alex's book cost than each ticket in
Gloria's book?

1. What is the question? _____

_____

2. What information do you know from the problem? _____

_____

_____

3. What else do you need to know to solve the problem? _____

_____

_____

4. Pick a number that tells how many tickets might have been in Alex's

economy book. _____

5. Now how much less did each ticket in Alex's book cost compared to

Gloria's book? _____

Problem 4 **The Flower Garden**

Louisa just planted a rectangular flower garden along
the side of her house. The garden measures 15 feet by 12 feet.
She wants to put a fence around the three open sides of
the garden. The fencing she has chosen costs $8.50 per foot.
How much will she have to pay for the fence?

1. What is the question? _____

_____

2. What information do you know from the problem? _____

_____

_____

3. What else do you need to know to solve the problem? _____

_____

_____

4. Pick three sides of the rectangular area you think Louisa is going to fence.

_____

_____

5. Now how much will the fence cost? _____

Problem 5 **The Ski Resort**

A ski resort has a lift that takes skiers to the top of the run. The lift can take eight skiers and their skis on each trip. If the ski lift opens at 7:30 a.m., how many skiers can it take to the top of the lift by noon?

1. What is the question?

_____

2. What information do you know from the problem? _____

_____

_____

3. What else do you need to know to solve the problem? _____

_____

_____

4. Pick a number that tells how long it might take the lift to complete

a round trip. _____

5. Now how many skiers would be able to reach the top of the lift by noon?

_____

Name
....

Problem 6 **The Basketball Game**

The Cardinals scored 68 points in a basketball game.
Gloria scored one-half of the points. Ellen, Laura,
and Martha scored the remaining points. Laura and
Ellen each scored the same number of points. How
many points did Martha score?

1. What is the question? _____

_____

2. What information do you know from the problem? _____

_____

_____

_____

3. What else do you need to know to solve the problem? _____

_____

_____

4. Pick a number that tells how many points Ellen and Laura might have scored.

_____

5. Now how many points would Martha have scored? _____

Name ....

Problem 7 **Baseball Equipment**

A baseball bat costs $12.00 more than a
baseball. Coach Reilly bought six baseballs
and three bats for the team. How much
did he spend?

1. What is the question? _____

_____

2. What information do you know from the problem? _____

_____

_____

3. What else do you need to know to solve the problem? _____

_____

_____

_____

4. Pick a number that tells how much it might cost to buy either a baseball

or a bat. _____

5. Now how much money would the coach have spent to buy baseball

equipment for the team? _____

© Wright Group/McGraw-Hill 0-7622-1351-5

Name
....

Problem 8 **The Pizza Shop**

The pictograph shows the number of pizzas sold last week by the Pizza Shop. Each circle represents a certain number of pizzas. How many pizzas were sold at the Pizza Shop last week?

Day	Pizzas Sold
Monday	
Tuesday	⦾ ⦾ ⦾ ⦾ ⦾
Wednesday	⦾ ⦾ ⦾ ⦾ ⦾ ⦾
Thursday	⦾ ⦾ ⦾ ⦾
Friday	⦾ ⦾ ⦾ ⦾ ⦾ ⦾ ⦾
Saturday	⦾ ⦾ ⦾ ⦾ ⦾ ⦾ ⦾ ⦾
Sunday	⦾ ⦾ ⦾ ⦾ ⦾

1. What is the question?

_____

_____

2. What information do you know from the problem? _____

_____

3. What else do you need to know to solve the problem? _____

_____

_____

4. Pick a number that tells how many pizzas each circle represents. _____

5. Now find out how many pizzas were sold last week. _____

_____

Name
....

Problem 9 **The Family Trip**

Last Sunday the Hayden family went on a trip
to the mountains. At noon they stopped for lunch.
Mr. Hayden bought four sandwiches at $1.75
each, four drinks at $1.00 each, and 4 brownies for
dessert. He gave the counterperson a $20.00.
How much change should Mr. Hayden receive?

1. What is the question? _____

_____

2. What information do you know from the problem? _____

_____

_____

3. What else do you need to know to solve the problem? _____

_____

_____

4. Pick a number that tells how much each brownie might have cost.

_____

5. Now how much change would Mr. Hayden receive back from his $20 bill?

_____

Name
....

Problem 10 **The Horse Stable**

The owner of a horse stable bought
96 pounds of hay for his horses to
eat during a one-week period. Each
horse ate the same amount of hay.
How much hay did each horse eat?

1. What is the question?

_____

_____

2. What information do you know from the problem? _____

_____

_____

3. What else do you need to know to solve the problem? _____

_____

_____

4. Pick a number that will tell how many horses the owner might have

had in his stable. _____

5. Now how much would each horse have eaten? _____

Answer Key

In this section students identify the question in the problem (#1). They state the information that is needed to solve the problem (#2) and determine the missing information that is preventing them from solving the problem (#3). They choose appropriate data to solve the problem (#4), and finally, they solve the problem (#5). The answers to #4 and #5 will vary depending on the data the student supplies.

Problem 1: Rolls of Film
1. How many pictures did Anita take on her trip?
2. She took 8 rolls of film. Some rolls contained 24 pictures and others contained 36 pictures.
3. The number of rolls that contained 24 pictures and the number that contained 36 pictures

Problem 2: Rain Gauge
1. What was the measure of the rain gauge at the end of the storm?
2. The amount of rain that had fallen after the first and second hour of the storm and the additional amount of rain measured at the end of the storm
3. The amount of rainfall measured by the gauge at the beginning of the storm

Problem 3: The County Fair
1. How much less did each ticket in Alex's book cost than each ticket in Gloria's book?
2. Gloria's book of 10 tickets cost $8.50. Alex's book cost $16.00.
3. The number of tickets in Alex's book

Problem 4: The Flower Garden
1. How much will Louisa pay for the fence?
2. The garden measures 15 ft × 12 ft. Fencing costs $8.50 per foot.
3. The measure of the three sides around which Louisa is planning to build the fence

Problem 5: The Ski Resort
1. How many skiers can get to the top of the lift by noon?
2. The lift can take 8 skiers on each trip.
3. The number of trips the lift can make from 7:30 to noon

Problem 6: The Basketball Game
1. How many points did Martha score?
2. There were 68 total points scored in the game. Gloria scored half of them. Laura and Ellen each scored the same number of points.
3. The number of points that were scored by Laura and Ellen

Problem 7: Baseball Equipment
1. How much did the coach spend for the baseballs and bats?
2. A baseball bat costs $12 more than a ball. The coach bought 6 baseballs and 3 bats.
3. The price of a baseball or the price of a bat

Problem 8: The Pizza Shop
1. How many pizzas were sold at the Pizza Shop last week?
2. Each circle on the graph represents a certain number of pizzas.
3. The number of pizzas represented by each circle

Problem 9: The Family Trip
1. How much change should Mr. Hayden receive from a $20 bill?
2. The number and cost of sandwiches and drinks he purchased
3. The cost of the brownies

Problem 10: The Horse Stable
1. How much hay did each horse eat?
2. The owner bought 96 pounds of hay for his horses. Each horse ate the same amount of hay.
3. The number of horses the owner had

Assessment Note
Students' work on any of the problems in this section can be assessed using the 3-step rubric on page viii.

Section 6 What's the Question if You Know the Answer?

THE MATHEMATICAL SITUATIONS in Section 6 do not include questions. With the exercises in the first half of this section, students are asked to choose which one of three questions presented can be answered from the data in the situation. In the second half, students progress to writing their own questions. This section encourages reasoning and the ability to work backward from a specific answer.

It is recommended that the teaching problem that follows be used as a whole-class activity.

The procedures outlined in the teaching problem will help students understand how to

a) identify a wide range of questions that can be constructed,

b) learn how to construct a question for a specific answer.

Working in small groups or in pairs is suggested as students learn to identify the correct question or to construct questions. This will allow them to discuss their thinking with one another. Once students are comfortable with the process, they can work independently.

Whole-group discussion is especially important in this section, even after students are working independently. A question based on specific information can be framed in various ways. Discussing what makes a good question and seeing well-constructed questions modeled will help students become more proficient at writing their own good questions. Students should also talk about how they arrive at a given answer. Knowing how to obtain the answer is crucial when constructing the question. It is important for the teacher as well as students to hear the thinking verbalized.

Mathematical Skills

Teaching Problem
Computation

Problem 1
Data Analysis, Addition, Subtraction

Problem 2
Addition, Subtraction, Multiplication

Problem 3
Addition, Subtraction

Problem 4
Addition

Problem 5
Probability

Problem 6
Data Analysis, Addition, Subtraction

Problem 7
Addition, Subtraction, Multiplication

Problem 8
Data Analysis, Addition, Subtraction

Problem 9
Addition, Subtraction, Multiplication

Problem 10
Data Analysis, Addition, Subtraction

The Flea Market

Teaching Goal

After participating in this lesson students should be able to generate a variety of questions based on the given data. They should be able to construct a question for a specific answer.

Problem

> Arlene loves to go to flea markets. One Saturday she found a booth at the market where old comic books were being sold. There were three piles of comic books. The first pile had 57 comic books that were marked 10¢ each. A second pile had 15 comic books marked 5¢ each. The third pile contained 36 comic books and was marked 2 for 35¢.

Teaching Plan

1. Write the problem on the overhead projector, whiteboard, or chalkboard.

2. Have the student read the problem.

3. This lesson can then take either a convergent or divergent approach.

Convergent Approach

Use the *convergent* approach to have students hone in on finding the correct question for a given answer. Give a specific answer based on the numerical data and ask them to find a question for that answer.

What's the question if the answer is 57?

What's the question if the answer is $1.90?

What's the question if the answer is 72?

What's the question if the answer is $12.75?

What's the question if the answer is 108?

4. After presenting an answer, instruct students to go back to the problem to find an appropriate question.

   If the answer is 72, what is the question?

   Here, students will need to look for combinations of available amounts together with operations that will yield a result of 72. They should note that this answer is not expressed in money.

5. More than one question might be possible for a given answer. Discuss this possibility with the class.

Divergent Approach

Use the *divergent,* or brainstorming, approach to have students use the numerical data and generate as many questions and answers from that data as possible.

4. Ask students to use the data and list as many questions, and their answers, as they can find.

5. Compile a list of answers students have recorded. Have them check their answers against those listed above to see which match. They should then identify appropriate questions for the answers listed.

6. If there are answers for which no question has been found, ask students to refer back to the problem to find an appropriate question.

....

This is an excellent reasoning exercise. Initially some students may have difficulty constructing questions that can be answered by a given number. If you find your students are having difficulty with this lesson, you might want to try an additional lesson or two with the whole class before asking students to continue working the next problems with a small group or in pairs.

Problem 1 **John's Burger Hut**

Here is the menu from John's
Burger Hut.

Menu	
Hamburger	$1.35
Hot dog.	$0.85
Pizza slice	$0.90
Fresh fruit.	$0.40
Milk	$0.50
Tax is included.	

1. What's the question if the answer
is $1.85?
Ring a, b, or c.

a. How much does it cost to buy
a hamburger and fresh fruit?

b. How much does it cost to buy
a hamburger and milk?

c. How much does it cost to buy a
slice of pizza, fresh fruit, and milk?

2. What's the question if the answer
is $0.70?
Ring a, b, or c.

a. If you bought milk and a slice
of pizza and gave the cashier $2.00,
how much change should you
receive?

b. If you bought a hamburger and
fresh fruit and gave the cashier
$2.00, how much change should
you receive?

c. If you bought a slice of pizza
and fruit and gave the cashier
$2.00, how much change should
you receive?

Name

Problem 2 **The Grocery Store**

Mrs. Sanchez bought three pounds of grapes
at $1.29 a pound, three pounds of peaches at
$1.69 a pound, and two bags of potatoes
at $1.09 a bag. She gave the checkout clerk
a $20 bill.

1. What is the question if
the answer is $5.07?
Ring a, b, or c.

a. How much did she spend for
the grapes?

b. How much did she spend for
the peaches?

c. How much did she spend for
the potatoes?

2. What is the question if the
answer is $8.88?
Ring a, b, or c.

a. How much did she pay for the
groceries all together?

b. How much did she pay for the
grapes and peaches?

c. How much change did
Mrs. Sanchez get back from her
$20 bill?

Problem 3 **The International Mailing**

When Liz was overseas, she mailed nine postcards and five letters to her friends back home. It cost 26¢ to mail a postcard and 43¢ to mail each letter.

1. What is the question if the answer is 17¢?

Ring a, b, or c.

a. How many pieces of mail did Liz send to her friends altogether?

b. How much more did it cost to mail the postcards than the letters?

c. How much more does it cost to mail a letter than a postcard?

2. What is the question if the answer is $2.15?

Ring a, b, or c.

a. How much did it cost to mail all the letters?

b. How much did it cost to mail all the postcards?

c. How much did it cost to mail both the letters and the postcards?

Problem 4 **Double Feature**

The local theater is showing a special double feature on Saturday morning. Mr. Amos plans to attend with his eleven-year-old daughter. Adult tickets to the special will cost $4.50 if purchased in advance and $5.50 if purchased at the door. Children under 12 will pay only $1.00. Popcorn is $2.25 for the large size and $1.50 for the smaller size. Soft drinks are $0.75.

1. What is the question if the answer is $3.00? Ring a, b, or c.

a. How much will it cost for Mr. Amos's daughter to attend the double feature and buy a small box of popcorn?

b. How much will Mr. Amos spend for a large popcorn and soft drink?

c. How much will it cost Mr. Amos to buy a small box of popcorn and a soft drink?

2. What is the question if the answer is $8.50? Ring a, b, or c.

a. How much will Mr. Amos spend if he purchases a ticket for himself and his daughter at the door and buys a small box of popcorn and a soft drink?

b. How much will Mr. Amos spend if he purchases a ticket for himself, his daughter, and two of her eleven-year-old friends in advance?

c. How much will he spend if he purchases a ticket for himself and his daughter in advance and buys a large-size popcorn and a soft drink?

Problem 5 **The Gumball Machine**

In a small gumball machine, there are eighteen gumballs. Six of them are white, five are green, three are red, and the rest are blue. Marcy put in a coin and got a gumball.

1. The answer is 4 out of 18.

Ring a, b, or c.

a. What is the probability of Marcy getting a blue gumball from the machine?

b. What is the probability of Marcy getting a white gumball from the machine?

c. What is the probability of Marcy getting a green gumball from the machine?

2. What is the question if the answer is 3 out of 18?

_____

_____

3. What is the question if the answer is 0 out of 18?

_____

_____

© Wright Group/McGraw-Hill 0-7622-1351-5

Name
....

Problem 6 **The Softball Game**

Here are the scores for each inning of last night's softball game.

Inning	1	2	3	4	5	6	7
Panthers	0	1	0	0	3	0	6
Lions	0	0	1	2	4	0	2

1. What is the question if the answer is 9?

_____

_____

_____

2. What is the question if the answer is 1?

_____

_____

_____

3. What is the question if the answer is the seventh inning?

_____

_____

_____

Problem 7 **The Busy Day**

Alexis had a very busy day yesterday. She went shopping and bought a CD for $11.50 and a pair of running shoes for $40.00. She babysat in the evening for three hours and was paid $5.50 per hour. When she returned home after babysitting she had $25.00 in her purse.

1. What is the question if the answer is $16.50?

_____

_____

_____

2. What is the question if the answer is $51.50?

_____

_____

_____

3. What is the question if the answer is $60.00?

_____

_____

_____

Name
....

Problem 8 **Pie Sales**

The bar graph shows the sales
of different types of pies
at the Homestyle Bakery for
the week of June 11–17.

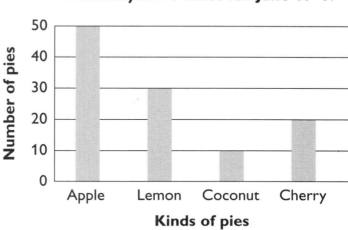

Homestyle Pie Sales for June 11–17

1. What is the question if the answer is 40? _____

_____

_____

2. What is the question if the answer is 110? _____

_____

_____

3. What is the question if the answer is 10? _____

_____

_____

Problem 9 Girls' Basketball League

Darlene plays basketball in the school league. Last night she was the high scorer for the team. She made five free throws that were worth one point each. She had seven field goals which were worth two points each, and she scored three three-point shots.

1. What is the question if the answer is 28 points?

_____

_____

_____

2. What is the question if the answer is 9 points?

_____

_____

_____

3. What is the question if the answer is 14 points?

_____

_____

Problem 10 **Recycling Drive**

Last week the students at Briana's school participated in a recycling drive by collecting aluminum cans. The table shows how many cans were collected each day.

Day	Number of Cans Collected
Monday	300
Tuesday	193
Wednesday	240
Thursday	186
Friday	231

1. What is the question if the answer is Monday?

_____

_____

_____

2. What is the question if the answer is 114?

_____

_____

_____

3. What is the question if the answer is 1,150?

_____

_____

_____

Answer Key

Problem 1: John's Burger Hut

1. b

2. c

Problem 2: The Grocery Store

1. b

2. c

Problem 3: The International Mailing

1. c

2. a

Problem 4: The Double Feature

1. b

2. c

Problem 5: The Gumball Machine

1. a

2. What is the probability of getting a red gumball?

3. What is the probability of getting a color other than blue, green, white, or red?

Only three questions are offered here for problems 6–10. Students should be encouraged to generate as many questions as possible. Remind students that it is possible to have more than one question for a given answer.

Problem 6: The Softball Game

1. What was the Lion's final score?

2. By how many runs did the Panthers beat the Lions?

3. In which inning were the most runs scored?

Problem 7: The Busy Day

1. How much did Alexis earn babysitting?

2. How much money did she spend on her shopping trip?

3. How much money did she have in her purse before she went shopping?

Problem 8: Pie Sales

1. What is the total number of lemon and coconut pies sold?

2. How many pies in all were sold that week?

3. How many more cherry pies than coconut pies were sold?

or

How many coconut pies were sold?

Problem 9: Girls' Basketball League

1. How many points were scored by Darlene altogether?

2. How many points did she score by making three-point shots?

3. How many points were scored by field goals?

or

How many points did Darlene score on free throws and three-point shots?

Problem 10: Recycling Drive

1. On which day were the most cans collected?

2. What is the difference between the number of cans collected on Monday and the number collected on Thursday?

3. What was the total number of cans collected?

Assessment Note

Students' work on any of the problems in this section can be assessed using the 3-step rubric on page viii.

 © Wright Group/McGraw-Hill 0-7622-1351-5